Multiplying and Dividing

Written by David Kirkby

Illustrated by John Haslam

This book belongs to

....

EGMONT

Tips for happy home learning

Make learning fun by working at your child's pace
and always giving tasks which s/he can do.
Tasks that are too difficult will discourage
her/him from trying again.

Give encouragement and praise and remember
to award gold stars and sticker badges for
effort as well as good work.

Always do a little rather than too much,
and finish each session on a positive note.

Don't work when you or your child
is tired or hungry.

Reinforce workbook activities and new ideas by
making use of real objects around the home.

EGMONT

We bring stories to life

Published in Great Britain by Egmont UK Limited,
239 Kensington High Street, London W8 6SA
This edition published 2008
© 2008 Egmont UK Limited
All rights reserved.
ISBN 978 1 4052 4009 3
3 5 7 9 10 8 6 4
Printed in Italy

Write in the missing numbers.

1 child	2	hands	1 x 2 =	2
2 children	4	hands	2 x 2 =	4
3 children		hands	3 x 2 =	
4 children		hands	4 x 2 =	
5 children		hands	5 x 2 =	
6 children		hands	6 x 2 =	

Say the number of hands, in order, without looking.

| 9 children | | hands | 9 x 2 = | |

 Note for parents: ensure your child understands that 1 x 2 means 1 lot of 2 and 2 x 2 means 2 lots of 2.

Write in the missing numbers.

8 ducks	16	feet	8 x 2 =	16	
7 ducks	14	feet	7 x 2 =	14	
6 ducks		feet	6 x 2 =		
5 ducks		feet	5 x 2 =		
4 ducks		feet	4 x 2 =		
3 ducks		feet	3 x 2 =		
2 ducks		feet	2 x 2 =		
1 duck		feet	1 x 2 =		

Say the number of feet, in order, without looking.

10 ducks ☐ feet   10 x 2 = ☐

The kangaroo jumps along the line in twos.

0 1 2 3 4 5 6 7 8 9 10 11 12 13 14 15 16 17 18 19 20

Write the numbers the kangaroo lands on.

2	4								

Colour the numbers the kangaroo lands on, and continue the pattern.

1	2	3	4	5	6
7	8	9	10	11	12
13	14	15	16	17	18
19	20	21	22	23	24
25	26	27	28	29	30
31	32	33	34	35	36

Can you see a pattern?

Write in the missing numbers.

1 stool	3	legs	1 x 3 =	3
2 stools	6	legs	2 x 3 =	6
3 stools		legs	3 x 3 =	
4 stools		legs	4 x 3 =	
5 stools		legs	5 x 3 =	
6 stools		legs	6 x 3 =	

Say the number of legs, in order, without looking.

8 stools		legs	8 x 3 =	

Note for parents: Ensure your child understands that 1 x 3 means 1 lot of 3 and 2 x 3 means 2 lots of 3.

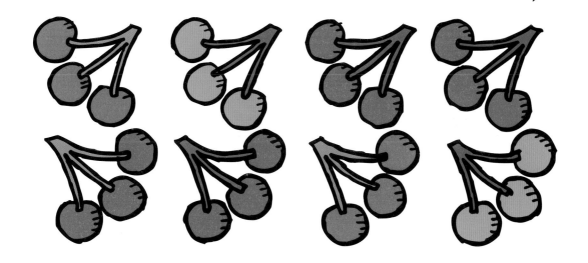

Write in the missing numbers.

8 bunches	24	cherries	8 x 3 =	24
7 bunches	21	cherries	7 x 3 =	21
6 bunches		cherries	6 x 3 =	
5 bunches		cherries	5 x 3 =	
4 bunches		cherries	4 x 3 =	
3 bunches		cherries	3 x 3 =	
2 bunches		cherries	2 x 3 =	
1 bunch		cherries	1 x 3 =	

Say the number of cherries, in order, without looking.

| 10 bunches | | cherries | 10 x 3 = | |

How many bunches are there in the picture?

The frog jumps along the line in threes.

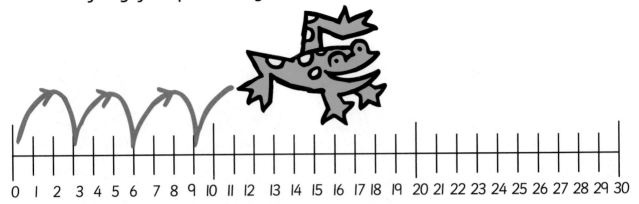

0 1 2 3 4 5 6 7 8 9 10 11 12 13 14 15 16 17 18 19 20 21 22 23 24 25 26 27 28 29 30

Write the numbers the frog lands on.

3	6	9							

Colour the numbers the frog lands on, and continue the pattern.

1	2	3	4	5	6
7	8	9	10	11	12
13	14	15	16	17	18
19	20	21	22	23	24
25	26	27	28	29	30
31	32	33	34	35	36

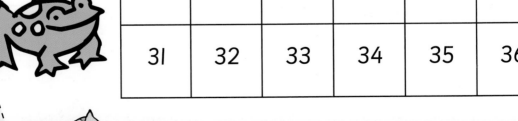

You have made another pattern!

Write in the missing numbers.

1 flower	4	petals		1 x 4 =	4
2 flowers	8	petals		2 x 4 =	8
3 flowers		petals		3 x 4 =	
4 flowers		petals		4 x 4 =	
5 flowers		petals		5 x 4 =	
6 flowers		petals		6 x 4 =	

Say the number of petals, in order, without looking.

| 9 flowers | | petals | | 9 x 4 = | |

Note for parents: Use real objects, such as buttons, pennies or real flower petals to help your child with this exercise.

Write in the missing numbers.

8 giraffes	32	legs	8 x 4 =	32
7 giraffes	28	legs	7 x 4 =	28
6 giraffes		legs	6 x 4 =	
5 giraffes		legs	5 x 4 =	
4 giraffes		legs	4 x 4 =	
3 giraffes		legs	3 x 4 =	
2 giraffes		legs	2 x 4 =	
1 giraffe		legs	1 x 4 =	

Say the number of legs, in order, without looking.

10 giraffes ☐ legs   10 x 4 = ☐

You are doing wonderfully well!

The grasshopper jumps along the line in fours.

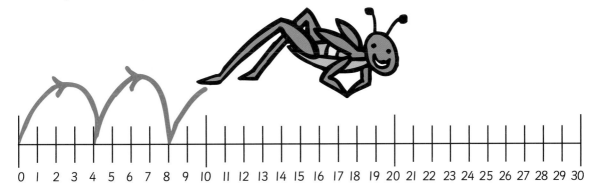

```
0  1  2  3  4  5  6  7  8  9  10  11  12  13  14  15  16  17  18  19  20  21  22  23  24  25  26  27  28  29  30
```

Write the numbers the grasshopper lands on.

4	8					

Colour the numbers the grasshopper lands on, and continue the pattern.

1	2	3	4	5	6
7	8	9	10	11	12
13	14	15	16	17	18
19	20	21	22	23	24
25	26	27	28	29	30
31	32	33	34	35	36

Note for parents: Ask your child to compare the pattern of fours with the pattern of twos. Which numbers are repeated?

Twos, threes, fours

Continue writing the patterns.

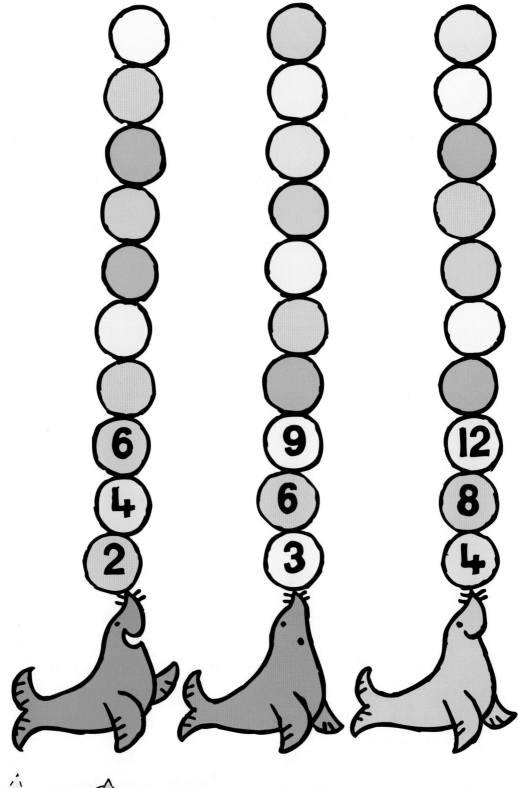

Write in the missing numbers.

1 foot	5	toes	1 x 5 =	5	
2 feet	10	toes	2 x 5 =	10	
3 feet		toes	3 x 5 =		
4 feet		toes	4 x 5 =		
5 feet		toes	5 x 5 =		
6 feet		toes	6 x 5 =		

Say the number of toes, in order, without looking.

8 feet ☐ toes   8 x 5 = ☐

How many swimmers can you count?

Write in the missing numbers.

8 stars	40	points	8 x 5 =	40
7 stars	35	points	7 x 5 =	35
6 stars		points	6 x 5 =	
5 stars		points	5 x 5 =	
4 stars		points	4 x 5 =	
3 stars		points	3 x 5 =	
2 stars		points	2 x 5 =	
1 star		points	1 x 5 =	

Say the number of points, in order, without looking.

| 9 stars | | points | 9 x 5 = | |

You are a super star!

The flea jumps along the line in fives.

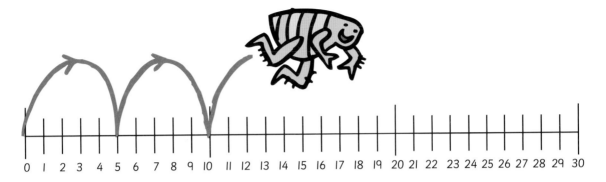

0 1 2 3 4 5 6 7 8 9 10 11 12 13 14 15 16 17 18 19 20 21 22 23 24 25 26 27 28 29 30

Write the numbers the flea lands on.

5	10				

Colour the numbers the flea lands on, and continue the pattern.

1	2	3	4	5	6	7	8	9	10
11	12	13	14	15	16	17	18	19	20
21	22	23	24	25	26	27	28	29	30
31	32	33	34	35	36	37	38	39	40
41	42	43	44	45	46	47	48	49	50
51	52	53	54	55	56	57	58	59	60
61	62	63	64	65	66	67	68	69	70
71	72	73	74	75	76	77	78	79	80
81	82	83	84	85	86	87	88	89	90
91	92	93	94	95	96	97	98	99	100

Is there a pattern this time too?

The toffees are shared equally between two children. Draw the toffees.

6 shared by 2 is 3 each

☐ shared by 2 is ☐ each

☐ shared by 2 is ☐ each

Note for parents: Ask your child to investigate whether all even numbers divide by two.

The cakes are shared equally between three plates.
Draw the cakes.

6 shared by 3 is 2 each

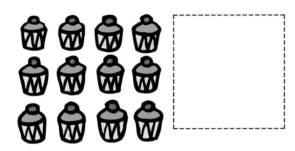

☐ shared by 3 is ☐ each

☐ shared by 3 is ☐ each

Note for parents: Use pencils, buttons or sweets to help your child with this activity.

★ **Twos**

Write down how much money is in each pile.

4 lots of 2p coins

4 x 2p = 8p

[ ] lots of 2p coins

[ ] x 2p = [ ]

[ ] lots of 2p coins

[ ] x 2p = [ ]

[ ] lots of 2p coins

[ ] x 2p = [ ]

[ ] lots of 2p coins

[ ] x 2p = [ ]

[ ] lots of 2p coins

[ ] x 2p = [ ]

Note for parents: Your child can work out these sums using real coins.

Write down how much money is in each pile.

| 3 | lots of 5p coins |

| 3 | x 5p = | 15p |

| | lots of 5p coins |

| | x 5p = | |

| | lots of 5p coins |

| | x 5p = | |

| | lots of 5p coins |

| | x 5p = | |

| | lots of 5p coins |

| | x 5p = | |

| | lots of 5p coins |

| | x 5p = | |

You are clever with coins!

Write in the missing numbers.

1 bar	10	pieces	1 x 10 =	10
2 bars	20	pieces	2 x 10 =	20
3 bars		pieces	3 x 10 =	
4 bars		pieces	4 x 10 =	
5 bars		pieces	5 x 10 =	
6 bars		pieces	6 x 10 =	

Say the number of pieces, in order, without looking.

9 bars		pieces	9 x 10 =	

 This is making me hungry!

Write down how much money is in each pile.

6 lots of 10p coins

6 x 10p = 60p

lots of 10p coins

x 10p =

lots of 10p coins

x 10p =

lots of 10p coins

x 10p =

lots of 10p coins

x 10p =

lots of 10p coins

x 10p =

You are getting good at this!

Write in the missing numbers.

1 box	6	eggs	1 x 6 =	6
2 boxes	12	eggs	2 x 6 =	12
3 boxes		eggs	3 x 6 =	
4 boxes		eggs	4 x 6 =	
5 boxes		eggs	5 x 6 =	
6 boxes		eggs	6 x 6 =	

Say the number of eggs, in order, without looking.

| 8 boxes | | eggs | 8 x 6 = | |

 Eggcellent work!

Continue writing the numbers in turn.

1	6							
2	7							
3								
4								
5								

1	7							
2	8							
3								
4								
5								
6								

Can you say the numbers in each bottom row, in order, without looking?

That was tricky, time for another star!

Fives, tens, sixes

Continue the patterns.

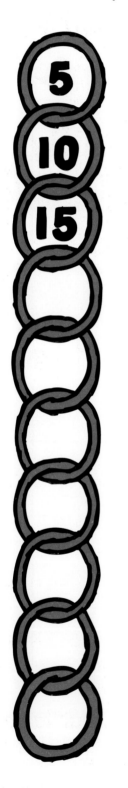 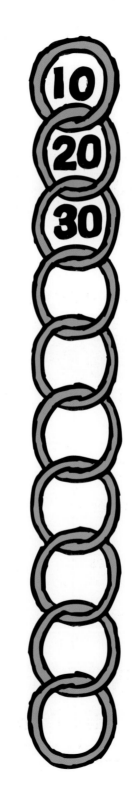 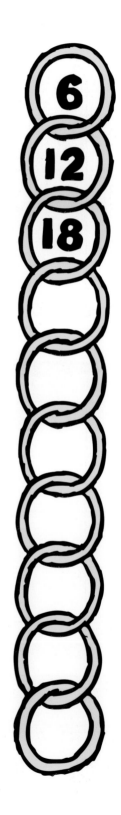

Note for parents: Compare the pattern of fives with the pattern of tens. Can you find any other patterns?

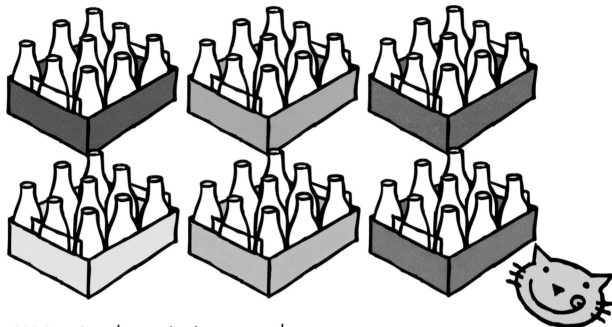

Write in the missing numbers.

1 crate	9	bottles	1 x 9 =	9
2 crates	18	bottles	2 x 9 =	18
3 crates		bottles	3 x 9 =	
4 crates		bottles	4 x 9 =	
5 crates		bottles	5 x 9 =	
6 crates		bottles	6 x 9 =	
7 crates		bottles	7 x 9 =	

Say the number of bottles, in order, without looking.

| 8 crates | | bottles | 8 x 9 = | |

What a lot of bottles!

Eights

Write in the missing numbers.

1 spider	8	legs	1 x 8 =	8
2 spiders	16	legs	2 x 8 =	16
3 spiders		legs	3 x 8 =	
4 spiders		legs	4 x 8 =	
5 spiders		legs	5 x 8 =	
6 spiders		legs	6 x 8 =	
7 spiders		legs	7 x 8 =	

Say the number of legs, in order, without looking.

9 spiders		legs	9 x 8 =	

How many did you get right?

Write in the missing numbers.

1 necklace	7	beads	1 x 7 =	7
2 necklaces	14	beads	2 x 7 =	14
3 necklaces		beads	3 x 7 =	
4 necklaces		beads	4 x 7 =	
5 necklaces		beads	5 x 7 =	
6 necklaces		beads	6 x 7 =	
7 necklaces		beads	7 x 7 =	

Say the number of beads, in order, without looking.

| 8 necklaces | | beads | 8 x 7 = | |

You deserve another gold star.

Continue the patterns.

7
14
21

8
16
24

9
18
27

Note for parents: Ask your child to look for patterns in the numbers.

The bones are shared equally between four dogs.
Draw the bones.

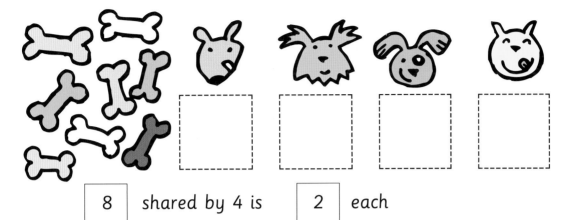

| 8 | shared by 4 is | 2 | each |

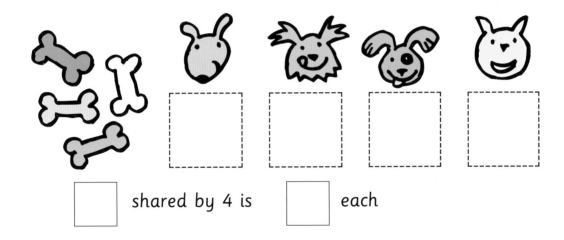

| | shared by 4 is | | each |

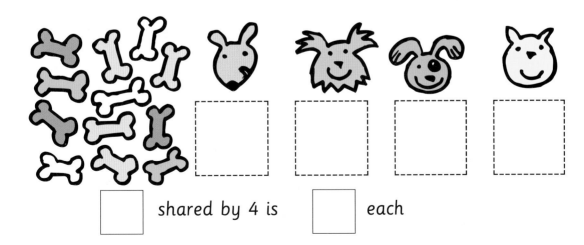

| | shared by 4 is | | each |

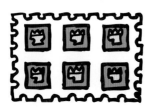

2 rows of 3 stamps

2 x 3 = 6

☐ rows of ☐ stamps

☐ x ☐ = ☐

☐ rows of ☐ stamps

☐ x ☐ = ☐

☐ rows of ☐ stamps

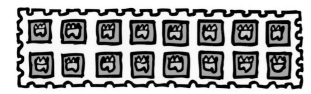

☐ x ☐ = ☐

Great work again!

3 rows of 4 pegs

3 x 4 = 12

☐ rows of ☐ pegs

☐ x ☐ = ☐

☐ rows of ☐ pegs

☐ x ☐ = ☐

☐ rows of ☐ pegs

☐ x ☐ = ☐

Multiplying

Write in the missing numbers in the multiplication square.

1	2	3	4	5	6	7	8	9	10
2	4	6	8	10	12	14			20
3	6	9	12	15				27	30
4	8	12					32	36	40
5	10		20	25			40	45	
6	12	18		30			48		60
7	14			35	42			63	70
8	16		32		48		64		80
9	18	27				63	72		90

Which numbers appear in the table four times?

You have finished the book, well done!